THIS BOOK BELONGS TO:

_____

_____

_____

SUPER HEARING

written by JENNIFER WHITEHEAD

pictures by EMILY REYMANN

ISBN 978-1-7368086-2-7

For my children, Brooks and Vivian.

And to my cheerleaders, Brandon and Lauren.
Without you this would forever be on my to-do list.

The world is filled with beautiful sounds,
I want to hear them all.

Morning birds
singing softly,
or the quiet drops
of rain fall.

I have a special superpower,
nestled in my ear.
I wear them proudly every day,
they help make noises clear.

I played a couple silly games,
listening for quiet tones.

And then they made an ear mold,
They'll do it again when it's outgrown.

Next I choose my favorite color,
right now I'm loving blue.
They express me just right,
and you can pick your favorite, too!

At first they felt a little funny,
when I wore them everyday.
But now they feel just right,
and don't bother me
when I play.

When I hear a quiet beep,
or see a small red light,

It's time to change my batteries,
or charge them overnight.

I can hear my friends swinging,
as I whiz down the slide.

We count and sing together,
while we spend the day outside.

If you notice my super ears
and want to know more,

Come on over, let's be friends!
I feel sad when I'm ignored.

Sometimes I need quiet time,
to take care of myself and rest.

I shut down my super ears,
this keeps me feeling my best.

Being different is beautiful,
my super ears set me apart.
We get to use our differences,
to learn and accept with a
growing heart.

I like sharing my superpower,
and I know you have one too.

Let's love ourselves and embrace the
things that make us me and you!

Made in United States
Orlando, FL
16 December 2022